The Monster in the Cupboard

Written by Narinder Dhami
Illustrated by Stephen Lewis

D0242489

Chapter 1

It was the first day of the new term. Emily and her best friend, Rosie, were glad to be back at school. But there was one thing they didn't like, and that was Kevin Brown.

'Look at Kevin,' Emily said. 'He thinks he's so cool.'

It was playtime, and Kevin was
running round the playground
very fast. He kept on bumping
into some of the other children,
and trying to push them over.

'Kevin Brown's just a great big
bully,' said Rosie. 'I wish he wasn't
in our class.'

There were lots of new
children in the playground. Some
of them looked scared because it
was their very first day at school.

'I'm glad I'm not a new kid,'
said Emily.

'Me too,' said Rosie.

Kevin Brown had stopped
running round the playground.
Now, he came over to a new boy
and girl, who were standing near
Emily and Rosie.

'Hey, you!' Kevin shouted at
the two little children. 'I'm the
king of this school, so you'd better
do what I say!'

The children looked scared, and Emily and Rosie felt sorry for them.

'Don't listen to him!' Emily told them. 'Kevin's not the king!'

'He's just a pain!' Rosie said.

Kevin glared at Emily and Rosie. 'You'd better shut up,' he said, 'or I'll tell them about the monster that lives in the empty classroom!'

'What monster?' asked the little boy.

'See that window?' Kevin said, with a big grin. 'That's the empty classroom. No one ever goes in there because the door's always locked. There's a big, dark cupboard inside, and that's where the monster lives!'

'What does the monster look like?' asked the new girl with a small voice.

'It's big and hairy and it's got long, sharp teeth!' Kevin said. 'And it can eat you up in one bite!'

'Stop it, Kevin!' said Emily. 'There isn't really a monster. You're just making it up!'

But the two new children still looked frightened.

'I'm scared of monsters!' said the little girl. 'I want to go home!' And she began to cry.

'I'm not scared,' said the little boy, but he looked very scared indeed.

'Now look what you've done, Kevin!' said Emily, crossly. But Kevin just laughed. He thought it was a great joke.

'You'd better stop crying!' he said. 'The monster in the cupboard doesn't like cry-babies. Look out, he's coming to get you!'

The boy and girl ran off.

'Why are you so mean, Kevin?' said Rosie. But Kevin just laughed even more.

'I'm going to tell all the new kids about the monster in the cupboard!' he said. 'I'm going to scare them all!'

'If you do, I'll tell the teachers,' Emily said.

Kevin stuck his tongue out at her.

'You'd better not!' he said, 'or you're in trouble!' And, suddenly, he jumped right into the middle of a big puddle. Emily was splashed with dirty water from top to toe, and she screamed.

'Kevin!' she shouted. 'Look what you've done to my new jumper!'

But Kevin didn't care one little bit. He just laughed and ran off.

'I'm fed up with Kevin Brown!' Emily said, crossly, as she looked down at her wet jumper. 'I'm going to teach him a lesson!'

Chapter 2

When they heard the bell, all the
children lined up to go back into
school. But Kevin Brown was still
going on about the monster in
the cupboard.

'You'd better watch out!' he
called to the new children. 'The
monster's waiting to jump out and
get you!'

'That does it,' said Emily.
'We've got to do something about
Kevin Brown!'

'Maybe we should tell Mr Bailey,' said Rosie. Mr Bailey was Rosie and Emily's new teacher.

As Kevin went past the empty classroom, he said, 'Look! This is where the monster lives!' He put his hand on the door. 'Shall I let the monster out?'

'No! No!' shouted all the new children.

'It's all right,' Emily told them. 'The door's always locked.'

But then Kevin tried the door handle and, suddenly, the door began to open! It opened very, very slowly, with a creaking sound. Everyone was shocked, even Kevin.

'The monster's coming!' shouted
one of the little children.

'No, it isn't!' Emily said. 'There's
no monster in there!'

'How do you know?'
Kevin asked.

'Because I don't believe in
monsters,' Emily said.

Kevin grinned. 'Go and look
inside the cupboard then!' he
told her.

Everyone went quiet when
Kevin said that, and they all
looked at Emily. Emily stared into
the dark, gloomy classroom and
the big cupboard in the corner. She
didn't really want to go in there, at
all. But then she saw the big grin
on Kevin's face.

'All right,' Emily said. 'I will!'
And she began to walk towards
the cupboard. But just then Mr
Bailey saw them.

'What's going on here?' he
asked. 'You should all be in class
by now. Off you go.'

Kevin looked annoyed. 'We'll
sneak back at lunchtime,' he said
to Emily. 'Then we'll see how
brave you are!'

'All right,' said Emily.

Mr Bailey gave the class some maths to do, but Emily got it all wrong. She couldn't stop thinking about the cupboard in the empty classroom. She didn't believe in monsters, but she still felt scared.

'Do you think there really is a monster?' Rosie asked her.

'No, of course not!' said Emily. But she wished lunchtime would never come. She looked over to the empty classroom. She told herself that there was nothing to be scared of. There wasn't a monster in there – was there?

'It's time for lunch, children,'
said Mr Bailey. 'Tidy your
tables, please.'

The bell rang, and Mr Bailey
hurried out of the room.
'I wonder where he's going
in such a hurry?' thought Emily.

'Come on!' said Kevin, who was
grinning all over his face. 'Let's go
and find the monster. He's
hungry – he wants his lunch!'

'Oh, very funny!' said Emily.

By the time Emily and Rosie got to the classroom, Kevin had told everyone that Emily was going to find the monster.

'You come with me, Kevin,' Emily said.

Kevin was going to say no, but then he had an idea. He could push Emily inside the big cupboard and lock her in! That would be a great laugh!

'All right, I will come with you,' he said, grinning.

Emily and Kevin walked slowly into the empty classroom. It was a bit dark in there and it felt a bit spooky. Then, suddenly, they heard a very strange noise. It was coming from the big cupboard in the corner!

Chapter 3

Emily and Kevin both stopped, and all the children who were watching, stood very still. Everyone listened.

Then they all heard it again. A scratching noise was coming from the cupboard in the corner.

'What's that?' Kevin asked.

'I don't know,' Emily said.

The scratching noise stopped. Then there was a thump. And then another.

THUMP! THUMP! THUMP!

'There IS something in the cupboard!' Kevin gasped. His face was white, and he was shaking all over.

'Let's find out what it is!' said Emily. She went over to the cupboard, but Kevin didn't follow her.

'Don't open that door, Emily!'
he said. 'The monster must be
in there!'

'No, Emily!' Rosie called.
'Don't open the door!'

'Don't open the door, Emily!'
called the little children.

And then everyone got a big
shock. Suddenly, the cupboard
door flew open.

'It's the monster!' Kevin shouted, and he ran for his life. He rushed for the door, bumping into tables and tripping over chairs. He pushed past the other children and ran off into the playground.

Emily didn't run. She stayed right where she was.

'What's going on out here?' said Mr Bailey, coming out of the cupboard.

He was carrying a big pile of
books. 'What's all this noise?' he
asked. Then he saw Emily.

'Hello, Sir,' said Emily. 'I
thought you might like some help
carrying the books.'

'Oh, thank you,' said Mr
Bailey. 'There are some more in
the cupboard.'

Emily looked inside the cupboard. It was very big, and she could walk right inside it. There were lots of books on the shelves, and it was a bit dark. But there was no monster.

Emily picked up the books and came out again. All the children were still watching and Emily smiled at them.

Mr Bailey told everyone to go
out into the playground. Emily
carried the books into their
classroom, and then she went
outside too. Kevin Brown was
sitting, looking grumpy. Everyone
was standing round, laughing
at him.

'It wasn't a monster, Kevin!' said Emily. 'It was only Mr Bailey.'

Kevin turned red. 'I knew that!' he said.

Everyone laughed even more.

'No, you didn't!' said Rosie. 'You ran off because you thought the monster was coming to eat you up!'

Kevin went off in a very bad mood.

'I don't think he'll be so mean from now on!' said Emily. 'And he won't tease the new kids so much!'

It was time for Emily and Rosie to eat their packed lunch.

'You were really brave, Emily,' said Rosie. 'Why didn't you run off like Kevin did?'

Emily smiled at Rosie. 'I knew it was Mr Bailey in the cupboard and not a monster!' she said.

'How?' Rosie asked.

'Because I saw Mr Bailey go into the empty classroom when the lunchtime bell rang,' Emily told her. 'That's why I asked Kevin to come in with me. I hoped that he'd hear Mr Bailey in the cupboard and think that he was the monster!'

Rosie began to laugh. 'Kevin would be really mad if he knew!' she said.

Emily grinned. 'It's our little secret!' she said.